Specialist publishers of price guide re

Roman Base I
A Price Guide.

By Richard J. Plant. 3rd Edition © MMVI

ISBN: 0-948964-47-2

A fully updated Price guide of over 630 base metal Roman coins dated 241 BC - 498 AD, with their market values in both British Pounds Sterling and US dollars, notes on changes in the coinage over the years, and over 640 drawings to aid identification.

The preceding 2nd edition of this book was ISBN 0-948964-46-4.

Errors and Omissions:

Every effort has been made to ensure that the information and price data contained within this book is accurate and complete. However, errors do sometimes have a habit of creeping in unnoticed, and with this in mind the following email address has been established for notifications of omissions and errors: info@rotographic.co.uk. Readers within the UK can also call the telephone number below.

This edition is dedicated to the authors grandchildren: Joshua, Jordan, Emily, Caleb and Leah.

www.rotographic.co.uk
0871 871 5122

In Association with

Contents

Preface to the 3rd edition

There is far more interest in history and in historical things than there used to be. The television is putting on all sorts of programmes about old-time battles; about "What the Romans did for us", and about antiques; and interest in coins is growing too – which means, for the more mercenary minded amongst us, that in the long-term prices are bound to keep on rising. This also means that NOW is a good time to be collecting coins, as even a bad buy now will probably turn out to have become a good buy in the years to come.

But please do not buy coins just for investment, as I think that that would be a waste of one of the world's strictly limited historical resources. Roman coins ought to be enjoyed! They are amongst the few ancient artefacts that the ordinary man in the street can reasonably hope to possess, and they can have the power to lift our imaginations above mundane 21st century matters back into Roman times. They can, to a certain extent, bring the Roman Empire back to life.

It is good that we have felt the need to price the coins in US dollars, as well as in British pounds; and as we can, if we wish, join chat groups on the Internet with people from all over the world, we realise, as we have not done before, that we numismatists are nowadays indulging in an international hobby.

Remember that we get out of any activity what we put into it. Do not let your coins just lie there, pick them up, handle them, read about them, and learn about them. If you act in this manner you will not be able to help enjoying your collection.

All best wishes, wherever you are, and I do hope that you find this little book helpful.

Richard J.Plant, Doncaster, England

Introduction

This is not a scholarly tome for the expert, and there are no amazing new theories to confront the reader. It is meant to be a book that will enable the ordinary coin collector, who perhaps owns only a few Roman coins, to find out as painlessly as possible what his coins are, and what they are worth. Its small size means that it can be slipped in a pocket and taken round the coin fair with you; and it may well be the sort of book in which you can write notes, or tick off the Emperors for whom you possess a coin.

All illustrations are as close to "life-size" as possible; but remember that we are not dealing with modern coins. I have drawn them as being circular for my convenience; but few of them are actually round. Worse, the lettering may not be as "joined up" as we are used to with modern writing. "N" may be III. "A" may look like H ; and "G" as C. In particular note that Roman "U" is V, and "J" is I. Emperors can face either way, and an Imperial portrait may vary considerably from one coin to the next.

Any book attempting to include every possible base metal coin minted by the Romans would have to be extremely large; so for this small (and inexpensive) catalogue I have concentrated on Obverses rather than Reverses, hopefully enabling the collector to attribute his coin to one definite Emperor, which should date the coin to within a few years. I feel that the majority of collectors will agree that in most cases the reverse design is of lesser importance for purposes of attribution..

Please note that all the reference numbers in this book begin with "CRB" to distinguish them from the "CRS" numbers used in "Roman Silver Coins".

A note on Pronunciation and plurals

The language of the Romans is known as "Latin"; but though this was to be the basis of a number of modern languages, such as Italian and Spanish, and though we do still possess a great deal of ancient Latin literature, nobody nowadays is really sure how the ancient Romans pronounced their words; and in any case you did not buy this book to learn a language, but to help identify your coins!

However, note that "C" ought to be as the "c" in "cake" and not like the "c" in "certainly"; so, if you were talking to a Roman you would have to pronounce "Caesar" like "Kaiser" (the same as the German for Emperor or King).

Note also the Latin plurals we use in this catalogue - the plural of Sestertius is Sestertii (pronounced Sestert-ee-ee) ; of Dupondius, Dupondii (Dupond-ee-ee): of Antoninianus, Antoniniani ; and of Follis, Folles.

The Valuations

Most collectors, particularly beginners, desperately want to know how much the coins they own are worth and, obviously, need a guide as to approximately how much they should pay for a coin. Note that any price system for Roman coins can only be a rough guide as to true value.

What is any individual coin worth? How come the variations between one catalogue and another? Basically, all pricing must be a matter of opinion, e.g. how much a dealer thinks a potential customer will be willing to pay. A coin may be of the highest rarity, but if nobody wants to buy it, it has no commercial value; whereas a relatively common coin may be highly sought after and, therefore, have a high valuation.

Larger coins tend to be more popular than smaller ones: so the Sestertius will, usually, be dearer than the Dupondius or As. Coins with a Christian link are popular, or coins with a British connection will, in Britain, be more highly priced. Thus Hadrian will be more expensive than Trajan because of Hadrian's Wall!

Condition

Unless otherwise stated, all coins of phase one and phase two are priced in Fine condition (i.e. up to 260 AD), and those of phases three, four and five in Very Fine.

PLEASE NOTE that in this book, the term "allegorical figure" is used in a very wide sense to include gods and goddesses and, even, sacrificial implements, as well as figures that are allegorical *in the usual sense*.

Note, also, that "as Fig.16" means that the figure described is very like the illustration; whereas "Similar to Fig.14" may indicate a different pose or different atributes.

Exchange Rate:

This book was priced in British Pounds Sterling . The US$ prices shown are for the benefit of American and international readers. The exchange rate used was GB£1.00 = US$1.80 with US$ values being rounded up or down to the nearest whole dollar, or to the nearest $5 where higher values are concerned.

4

Drawings of the common Roman Reverse types

During much of the Roman Empire, coin reverses commonly depict an allegorical figure or a diety. The following list is by no means exhaustive of such types and, though the poses of particular figures may vary considerably, even within the same reign, it is hoped that these drawings may help the collector. When a 'Fig.' is referred to it relates to the reverse types on these pages.

Fig.1
Abundantia

Fig.2
Aequitas *and*
Moneta

Fig.3
Adventus

Fig.4
Aeternitas

Fig.5
Annona

Fig.6
Comes

Fig.7
Concordia

Fig.8
Felicitas

Fig.9
Fides Militum

Fig.10
Fortuna

Fig.11
Genius

Fig.12
Hilaritas

Fig.13
Juno

Fig.14
Jupiter

Fig.15
Laetitia

Fig.16
Liberalitas

Fig.17
Libertas

Fig.18
Mars

Fig.19
Marti Pacifero

Fig.20
Minerva

| Fig.21 Oriens *and* Sol *and* Invictus | Fig.22 Pax | Fig.23 Pietas | Fig.24 Pietas Augustor (Sacrificial Implements) | Fig.25 Providentia |

| Fig.26 Principi Iuventutis | Fig.27 Pudicitia | Fig.28 Romae Aeternae | Fig.29 Salus | Fig.30 Salus |

| Fig.31 Securitas | Fig.32 Spes | Fig.33 Uberitas | Fig.34 Venus | Fig.35 Vesta |

Fig.36
Victoria

Fig.37
Virtus

Variations

On the coins the figure may be named; for example. Fig.32 may be SPES AUG or SPES AUGUSTI: "the hope provided by the Emperor", or SPES PUBLICA. Fig.8 may be FELICITAS AUG: "the prosperity provided by the Emperor", or FELICITAS TEMPORUM: "the prosperity of the times".

It helps to remember that there was no mass media in Roman times, and the coins were an important means of putting the official line over to the populace. PAX AUG may not mean that the Emperor has really provided peace, but that he wants people to think that he is going to provide peace!

As allegorical types came to be recognised by pose and attributes they did not need to be actually named on every coin. The reverse often consists of the Emperor's titles (e.g. P.M. TR.P.IIII COS, III P.P.) around an allegorical figure.

PHASE ONE

The Republic

Rome was traditionally founded in 753 BC, and in its earliest period was ruled by Kings. The last of these, Tarquin the Proud, was expelled in 509 BC when a Republic was set up led by two annually elected Consuls.

Although the outward forms of the Republic lasted longer, it is convenient to date its end as being 31 BC when Octavian defeated Mark Antony, his last rival for power, at the Battle of Actium. After this he was able to initiate procedures which resulted in his becoming the Emperor Augustus.

Although the Republican period is wonderfully rich with regard to the diversity of its silver coinage, It is very poor when it comes to bronze.

We pass over the early irregular lumps of metal known as AES RUDE and the heavy quadrilateral bars called AES SIGNATUM, to arrive at the heavy cast coins with a design on both Obverse and Reverse, the AES GRAVE, which were in use during much of the Third Century BC. Normally, none of these are met with by the collector!

The earliest coins the collector is likely to encounter are named according to a denomination more usually found in Sicily: the LITRA.

241-235 BC

CRB1: Litra, **Fine £35/\$63**	**CRB2**: Half Litra, **Fine £40/\$72**	**CRB3**: Quarter Litra, Fine **£28/\$50**

The regular bronze coinage of the Republic consists of coins bearing the head of a deity on the Obverse, a different deity for each denomination, and the prow of a galley on the Reverse. From the AS, marked with a 'I', down to the UNCIA, marked with a dot; denominations are marked on both the Obverse and the Reverse.

There are, also, a few early coins which are not of the usual Diety/Prow pattern, but are on the Roman Standard (where 12 UNCIAE make 1 AS).

217-215 BC

CRB5: Semuncia, **Fine £35/\$63**

CRB4: Uncia, **Fine £72/\$130**

The Republic

All this sounds easy so far! The difficulty lies in the decreasing weight standards:

A.   The LIBRAL standard, c240 - 217 BC, with the AS (at this stage still an AES GRAVE cast coin) weighing anything between 212 and 248 grammes.
B.   SEMI-LIBRAL, c217 - 215 BC, with the AS at 99 to 162 grammes.
C.   TRIENTAL, 215 - 212 BC, with the AS at 52 to 73 grammes.
D.   SEXTANTAL, 211 - 155 BC, the AS at 25 to 44 grammes.
E.   UNCIAL, 155 - 124 BC, the AS now down to 17 grammes or so.
F.   SEMUNCIAL, 90 - 75 BC, with the AS around 13 grammes.

So, how can one price a Republican AS? Obviously, size must be an important factor, with larger coins dearer, in general, than smaller versions of the same denomination. The illustrations are taken from differing series, with the particular series for each given in brackets.

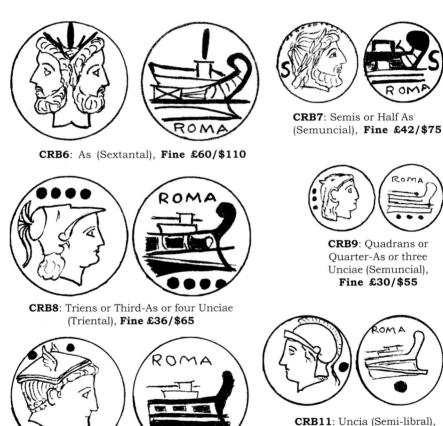

CRB6: As (Sextantal), **Fine £60/$110**

CRB7: Semis or Half As (Semuncial), **Fine £42/$75**

CRB8: Triens or Third-As or four Unciae (Triental), **Fine £36/$65**

CRB9: Quadrans or Quarter-As or three Unciae (Semuncial), **Fine £30/$55**

CRB10: Sextans or two Unciae (Triental), **Fine £30/$55**

CRB11: Uncia (Semi-libral), **Fine £30/$55**

The Republic

CRB12: Semuncia (Semi-libral - This denomination was discontinued in the later periods) No marks of face value, **Fine £30/$55**

CRB13: Quartuncia (Semi-libral period only) No marks of face value, **Fine £30/$55**

Many of these coins are marked with symbols, monograms or names. This adds value in the order of, perhaps, £5.

CRB14: As - Obv as CRB6, **Fine £65/$115**

Imperatorial Period

The Imperatorial period comes towards the end of the Republic when the great men, such as Pompey and Caesar, were contending for power, and when coins bearing names of such leaders were being produced. Most of these are in silver; but there are a few of base metal.

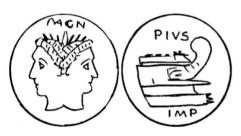

CRB15: As - Obv shows head of Pompey treated as a Janus-head (minted by Sextus Pompey in Sicily 45BC), **Fine £95/$170**

CRB16: Sestertius (4 Asses). Minted in Italy by the order of Octavian who later became Emperor Augustus. Obv shows head of Octavian, the Rev shows head of Julius Caesar, **Fine £200/$360**

PHASE TWO

The Early Empire

During this phase, lasting from 31 BC to around 260 AD, base metal denominations are in common usage; but, confusingly, of only four sizes. The large one is the Sestertius, of four Asses, made of a yellow metal called orichalcum. The two smallest are the Half-As or Semis, also made from orichalcum and the Quarter-As or Quadrans of copper (which looks much redder than orichalcum, when untarnished). The Semis is usually larger than the Quadrans - so there is not too much confusion there. The difficulty comes with the As itself and its double, the Dupondius which are the *same size*. All very well with newly minted coins because the As is of red copper and the Dupondius of yellow orichalcum; but the passage of time means that when we get them, they often both look the same.

In Nero's reign (54 - 68 AD), the practice began of giving the Emperor's portrait, on the obverse, a radiate crown for the Dupondius denomination and a laurel-wreath for the As, and this became the general rule for Emperors. Unfortunately, there is never any distinction in the case of the bare-headed Caesars or the earlier ladies. On later coins featuring ladies, a crescent by their shoulders indicates a Dupondius.

Note that during this period all base metal coins bear the initials S.C. (by the decree of the Senate); those without such letters are likely to be Colonial. Note, also, that where illustrations show names of magistrates or imperial titles, these are usually variable.

AUGUSTUS, 31 BC - 14 AD
Period 1 - His Lifetime

CRB17: Sestertius - **Fine**
£90/$160

CRB18: Dupondius -
Fine £38/$68

CRB19: As - **Fine £42/$75**

CRB20: Dupondius - **Fine £42/$75**

AUGUSTUS, 31 BC - 14 AD
Period 1 - His Lifetime

CRB21: As of Lugdunum
(Gaul) - **Fine £35/$63**

CRB22: Quadrans -
Fine £17/$30

CRB21A: Semis, as CRB21 but smaller
- **Fine £30/$55**

CRB23: Quadrans -
Fine £18/$32

CRB24: Quadrans -
Fine £17/$30

CRB25: Quadrans -
Fine £17/$30

AUGUSTUS, 31 BC - 14 AD
Period 2 - Commemorative

Note, that after death, an Emperor officially became DIVUS, or "Divine".

CRB26: Sestertius (Rev names Tiberius) -
Fine £180/$325

CRB27: Dupondius (Minted under Caligula)
- **Fine £90/$160**

CRB28: As, Altar reverse (Minted under
Tiberius) - **Fine £36/$65**

CRB29: As (Minted under Tiberius) -
Fine £36/$65

AUGUSTUS, 31 BC - 14 AD
Period 2 - Commemorative (continued)

CRB30: As, thunderbolt reverse (Minted under Tiberius) - **Fine £42/$75**

CRB31: As, Livia seated reverse (Minted under Tiberius) - **Fine £42/$75**

TIBERIUS, 14 - 37 AD
Period 1 - Minted under Augustus

CRB32: As - **Fine £48/$85**

CRB33: As of Lugdunum - **Fine £45/$80**

CRB33A: Semis (as CRB33 but smaller) - **Fine £40/$72**

Period 2 - From 14 AD

CRB34: Dupondius - **Fine £150/$270**

CRB35: As - **Fine £50/$90**

CRB36: As - **Fine £48/$85**

CRB37: As - **Fine £42/$75**

CALIGULA, 37 - 41 AD

CRB38: Sestertius - **Fine £240/$430**

CRB40: Quadrans - **Fine £24/$45**

CRB39: As - **Fine £65/$115**

Friends and Relations of the Emperors 31 BC - 41 AD
(Augustus to Caligula)

LIVIA - Wife of Augustus, mother of Tiberius. Died 29 AD.

CRB41

CRB41 - 43: All are Dupondii (The plural for
Dupondius). Reverse types are all similar to
CRB41 - **Fine £96/$175 each**

CRB42   CRB43

AGRIPPA - Friend of Augustus. Died 12 BC

CRB44: As - **Fine £42/$75**

Friends and Relations of the Emperors 31 BC - 41 AD
(Augustus to Caligula) - Continued

DRUSUS - Son of Tiberius. Died 23 AD

CRB45: As - **Fine £62/$110**

ANTONIA - Grandmother of Caligula, mother of Claudius. Died 37 AD

CRB46: Dupondius -
Fine £96/$175
(Minted under Claudius)

GERMANICUS - Father of Caligula. Died 19 AD

CRB47: Dupondius - **Fine £96/$175**

CRB48: As - **Fine £55/$98**
(Minted under Caligula)

CRB49: As - **Fine £55/$98**
(Minted under Claudius)

Friends and Relations of the Emperors 31 BC - 41 AD
(Augustus to Caligula) - Continued

AGRIPPINA Senior - Mother of Caligula. Died 33 AD

CRB50: Sestertius - **Fine £300/$540**   **CRB51**: Sestertius - **Fine £260/$470**
(Reverse similar to CRB49)

NERO and DRUSUS - Brothers of Caligula. Died 31 and 33 AD

CRB52: Dupondius - **Fine £95/$170**

CLAUDIUS I - 41 - 54 AD

Important Note:

From this reign onwards, the varying obverse heads and imperial legends are grouped together at the beginning of each reign, or period of reign. They are meant to be taken as a sort of 'Pick-N-Mix'. Most head shapes may be used for most denominations (except of course, with regards to a radiate crown), and most legends may be used in conjunction with most of the head shapes on any of the denominations.

Obverse A

Obverse B

CLAUDIUS I - 41 - 54 AD (continued)

CRB53: Sestertius - **Fine £120/$215**
(Always with obverse A)

CRB55: Dupondius - **Fine £48/$85**
(Always with obverse B)

CRB56: As -
Fine £48/$85

CRB57: As -
Fine £36/$65

With legend:
LIBERTAS
AUGUSTA

CRB58: As -
Fine £42/$75
(Reverse as Fig.17)

CRB59: Quadrans - **Fine £18/$32**

CRB60: Quadrans - **Fine £18/$32**

CRB61: Barbaric copy of CRB57 - **Fair £12/$22 - £18/$32**

NERO - 54 - 68 AD

Note, that during this period, Emperors tend to use the name of their predecessor as well as their own. Thus, NERO is NERO CLAVDIVS. During this reign, the Dupondius starts to have a radiate head obverse (the spiky-looking head-dress as in obverse 2, below).

Obverse A　　　　　　**Obverse B**　　　　　　**Obverse C**

CRB62: Sestertius -
Fine £190/$340
(Always with obverse A)

CRB63: Sestertius -
Fine £120/$215

CRB64: Dupondius -
Fine £65/$115
(Always with obverse B)

CRB65: Dupondius - **Obverse B. Reverse similar to Fig.6.** Reverse legend reads: VICTORIA AVGVSTI - **Fine £48/$85**

CRB66: As, The temple of Janus is shown on the reverse. Obverse head is laureate and facing right - **Fine £70/$125**

CRB67: As, Reverse shows Nero as Apollo - **Fine £60/$110**

CRB68: As - **Fine £33/$60**

NERO - 54 - 68 AD (continued)

CRB69: As -
Fine £35/$63

CRB70: Semis -
Fine £24/$43
(Always with Nero obverse C)

CRB71: Quadrans -
Fine £24/$43

GALBA - 9/6/68 - 15/1/69 AD

Obverse A

Obverse B

CRB72: Sestertius -
Fine £180/$325
(Always with obverse A)

CRB73: Sestertius -
Reverse similar to Fig.17
Reverse legend reads:
LIBERTAS PVBLICA -
Fine £175/$315

CRB74: Dupondius -
**Obverse A. Reverse
similar to Fig.22**
Reverse legend reads: PAX
AVGVSTI -
Fine £60/$110

CRB75: As - **Obverse B.
Reverse similar to fig.17**
Reverse legend reads:
LIBERTAS PVBLICA -
Fine £60/$110

CRB76: As - **Obverse B.**
(Reverse as CRB39)
- **Fine £60/$110**

VITELLIUS - 2/1/69 - 20/12/69 AD

CRB77: As - **Fine £125/$225**

VESPASIAN - 69 - 79 AD

Obverse A

Obverse B

Obverse C

CRB78: Sestertius -
Fine £85/$155
(Always with obverse A)

CRB79: Sestertii, Various
Allegorical, e.g:
fig.10 reverse with legend:
FORTVNAE REDUCI

fig.22 reverse with legend:
PAX AVGVSTI

fig.32 Spes reverse with
imperial titles around it.

fig.18 reverse.

- Fine £65/$115 each

CRB80: Dupondius -
Fine £30/$55
(Always with obverse B)

CRB81: Dupondius -
Fine £30/$55
(Always with obverse B)

CRB82: Dupondii -
Various Allegorical, e.g:

figs. 7, 8, 10

- Fine £24/$45 each

CRB83: As -
Fine £110/$200
(Always with obverse C)

CRB84: As -
Fine £24/$43
(Always with obverse C)

CRB85: As, altar reverse
- **Fine £24/$43**
(Always with obverse C)

CRB86: As - Various
Allegorical, e.g:

Fig. 2 with legend:
AEQVITAS AVGVST

- Fine £24/$43 each

TITUS - 79 - 81 AD

His coins are very difficult to distinguish from those of his father Vespasian. Look for the abbreviation 'T' before CAES.

Period 1. As Caeser 69-79 AD

Obverse A	Obverse B	Obverse C

CRB87: Sestertius - Obverse A with Fig. 32 reverse - **Fine £115/$205**

CRB88: Dupondii - Obverse B or C but with radiate crown. With Fig. 28 reverse and legend: FELICITAS PVBLICA ROMA - **Fine £36/$65 each**

CRB89: Asses - Obverse B or C. With Fig. 2 reverse and legend: AEQVITAS AVGVSTI. Or with reverse legend: PAX AVGVST, showing Pax leaning on a column - **Fine £36/$65 each**

Period 2. As Augustus 79-81 AD

Obverse D	Obverse E

CRB90: Sestertii - Obverse D. Various reverse Allegorical types:

Fig. 5 with legend: ANNONA AVG

Fig.8 with legend: FELICIT PVBLIC

Fig.22 with legend: PAX AVGVST

Fig.32 reverse.
- **Fine £110/$200 each**

CRB91: Dupondii - Obverse E. Various reverse Allegorical types:

Fig. 7 with legend: CONCORDIA

Fig.29 with legend: SALVS AVG

Similar to Fig.5 with legend: CERES AVGVST
- **Fine £30/$55 each**

CRB92: Asses - Smaller version of obverse D. Various reverse Allegorical types:

Fig. 2 with legend: AEQVITAS AVGVST

Fig.11 with legend: GENI P.R.

Fig.32 Spes reverse
- **Fine £30/$55 each**

JULIA TITI - Daughter of Titus. Died c 91 AD

CRB93: Dupondius - **Fine £150/$270**

DOMITIAN - 81 - 96 AD

Another son of Vespasian

Obverse A   **Obverse B**

CRB94: Sestertii, Allegorical:

Spes Fig.32 reverse or reverse as CRB57 with larger version of obverse A or B.

Fine £90/$160 each

CRB95: Dupondii, with obverse A or B. Allegorical:

Fig.8 reverse with legend: FELICITAS PUBLICA

Fig.5 reverse with legend: CERES AVGVST

Fig.7 reverse with legend: CORCORDIA AVG

Fine £24/$43 each

CRB98: As - Fig.32 Spes reverse - **Fine £24/$43**

CRB96: As - **Fine £24/$43**   **CRB97**: As - **Fine £24/$43**

Period 2. As Augustus from 81 AD

Obverse C   **Obverse D**   **Obverse E**   **Obverse F**

DOMITIAN - 81 - 96 AD

CRB101: Sestertii with reverses similar to Fig.18 and Fig.20 - **Fine £90/$160 each**

CRB99: Sestertius - **Fine £145/$260** (Always with Obverse C)

CRB100: Sestertius - **Fine £90/$160**

CRB103: Dupondii with reverse legend: FIDEI PVBICAE or as CRB131 with legend: VIRTVTI AVGVSTI

- **Fine £24/$43 each**

CRB102: Sestertius - **Fine £75/$135** (Always with Obverse E)

CRB104: As - **Fine £72/$130** (Always with Obverse similar to C)

CRB105: Asses with Allegorical reverses:

Fig.10 with legend: FORTVNAE AVGVSTI. Fig.14 with legend: IOVI CONSERVAT. Fig.2 with legend: MONETA AVGVSTI. And reverses similar to CRB28 (but legend: SALVTI AVGVST) and CRB57 - **Fine £20/$35 each**

CRB106: Semis - **Fine £36/$65**

CRB107: Semis - **Fine £30/$55**

CRB108: Quadrans - **Fine £24/$43**

CRB109: Quadrans - **Fine £24/$43** (Obverse as CRB108)

CRB110: Quadrans - **Fine £24/$43**

Anonymous Quadrantes,
Domitian - Antoninus Pius
(81 - 161 AD)

CRB111:
Fine £22/$40

CRB112:
Fine £22/$40
(and others similar)

NERVA - 96 - 98 AD

Obverse A   Obverse B

CRB113: Sestertii
(Obverse B, but larger).
Allegorical:

Fig.17 reverse with legend:
LIBERTAS PVBLICA

Fig.22 reverse with legend:
PAX AVG
- **Fine £145/$260 each**

CRB114: Dupondius
(Obverse A).
Allegorical:

Fig.10 reverse with
legend:
FORTVNA AVGVST
- **Fine £40/$72**

CRB115: Asses
(Obverse B). Allegorical:

Fig.2 reverse with legend: AEQVITAS AVGVST.

Reverse similar to CRB77

Fig.17 reverse with legend: LIBERTAS PVBLICA
- **Fine £48/$85**

CRB116: Quadrans
- **Fine £24/$43**

TRAJAN - 98 - 117 AD

From now on there is such a multiplicity of reverse types that the common 'allegorical types' (in the wide sense of the term including deities etc) will be grouped together. Such coins do not usually vary much in valuation.

Trajan and Hadrian can be easily confused, because Hadrian is often: TRAIANVS HADRIANVS, and the two emperors can look alike. The titles: OPTIMO on the obverse and SPQR OPTIMO PRINCIPI on the reverse, are used only by Trajan.

Obverse A   Obverse B   Obverse C   Obverse D   Obverse E

TRAJAN - 98 - 117 AD

CRB117: Sestertius
(Obverse A and similar).
The reverse shows the
Danube bridge -
Fine £220/$395

CRB118:
Sestertius
- **Fine £110/$200**
(and similar
"political" types)

CRB121: Other allegorical
type dupondii
- **Fine £24/$43**

CRB119: Sestertius
- **Fine £54/$97**
(and other allegorical types)

CRB120:Dupondius
- **Fine £24/$43**
(always obverse B)

CRB122: As -
Fine £24/$43
(always obverse C)

CRB123: As -
Fine £22/$40
(and other allegorical types)

CRB124: Orichalcum As
- **Fine £30/$55**
(always obverse D)

CRB125: Semis.
A smaller version of CRB124
- **Fine £24/$43**
(always obverse D)

CRB126: Semis -
Fine £24/$43
(always obverse E)

CRB127: Quadrans
- **Fine £24/$43**

HADRIAN - 117 - 138 AD

Obverse A   Obverse B   Obverse C   Obverse D

CRB128: Sestertius -
Fine £90/$160
(always obverse B)

CRB129: Sestertius -
Fine £65/$115
(always obverse A)

CRB130: Sestertii.
Imperial and allegorical
types
- From £36/$65 Fine

CRB131: Dupondius
- Fine £26/$47
(always obverse C)

CRB132: As.
BRITANNIA reverse
- Fine £96/$175

CRB133: As
- Fine £50/$90

CRB134: As
- Fine £60/$110

CRB132 - 134 all have obverse head D, but with any of the obverse legends.

CRB135: As
- Fine £26/$47

CRB136: As -
Fine £26/$47
(and other allegorical types)

CRB137: Orichalcum As
- Fine £24/$43
(always obverse B)

CRB138: Quadrans
- Fine £26/$47

SABINA - Wife of Hadrian. Died c 136 AD

Obverse A   **Obverse B**   **Obverse C**

Both hair styles and both legends are used for all three denominations. The ladies hair styles are not an indication of the denomination.

Reverse types are allegorical, the commonest are: Fig.7 with legend: CONCORDIA. Pietas seated (similar to Fig.23) with legend: PIETAS. A reverse similar to CRB39 with legend VESTA. Ceres seated. And, Fig.34 with legend: VENVS GENETRICI.

CRB139: Sestertii - Fine £90/$160 each

CRB140: Dupondii - Fine £35/$63 each

CRB141: Asses - Fine £35/$63 each

AELIUS - Adopted son of Hadrian. Caesar 136 - 138 AD

CRB143: Sestertii. Allegorical types:

Fig.7 with legend: CONCORD

Fig.32 (Spes)

CRB142: Sestertius - Fine £130/$235 (reverse similar to CRB144)

- Fine £100/$180 each

CRB144: As - Fine £60/$110

CRB145: Allegorical Dupondii and Asses, around £52/$95 each Fine.

ANTONINUS PIUS - 138 - 161 AD

Period 1, as Caesar early 138 AD

CRB146: Sestertius - Fine £48/$85

Obverse A

Period 2, as Augustus

Obverse B

Obverse C

Obverse D

CRB147: Sestertius
- **Fine £480/$865**
(BRITANNIA reverse)

CRB148: Sestertius
- **Fine £145/$260**

CRB149: Sestertius
- **Fine £65/$115**

CRB150: Sestertii. Allegorical
types - **Fine £35/$63**

CRB151: Dupondii and Asses.
- **Fine £24/$43**
(Dupondii with obverse D)

Other types are often dearer
according to interest. BRITANNIA
type - **from £35/$63 Fine**

CRB152: Semis or Quadrans.
- **Fine £24/$43**
(obverses similar to obverse B)

Period 3, Commemorative

Obverse E

CRB153: Sestertius
- **Fine £60/$110**

CRB154: Sestertius
- **Fine £65/$115**

CRB155: As. Smaller
version of CRB154
- **Fine £35/$63**

FAUSTINA I - Wife of Antonius Pius. Died 141 AD

She lost her title "Augusta" in 147 AD when Faustina II took it.
(easily distinguishable from Faustina II by the hairstyle)

Period 1, Her lifetime

Obverse A

CRB156: Sestertius

Fig.34 reverse, with legend:
VENERI AVGVSTI

- **Fine £55/$100**

CRB157: As

Similar to Fig.13 reverse,
with legend:
IVNONI REGINAE

- **Fine £25/$45**

Period 2, Commemorative

Obverse B

Obverse C

Obverse D

CRB158: Sestertii.
Allegorical types
- **Fine £35/$63**
(with obverse B or C)

CRB159: Dupondii and
Asses. Allegorical types
- **Fine £22/$40**
(with obverse B, C, or
rarer, D)

MARCUS AURELIUS - 161 - 180 AD

Period 1, as Caesar 139 - 161 AD

Obverse A

CRB160: Sestertii.
Allegorical types -
Fine £40/$72

CRB161: Dupondii and Asses.
Allegorical types -
Fine £36/$65

Period 2, as Augustus

Obverse B	Obverse C	Obverse D

CRB162: Sestertii.
Allegorical types -
Fine £48/$85
(other types dearer,
according to interest)

Obverse E	Obverse F

CRB164: Dupondii
(radiate bust) and Asses.
Allegorical types -
Fine £22/$40

CRB163: As. Reverse
shows River Tiber
reclining -
Fine £48/$85

Period 3, Commemorative

Obverse G

CRB165: Sestertius.
- **Fine £60/$110**

CRB166: Sestertius.
- **Fine £60/$110**

CRB167: As. Smaller
version of CRB165 -
Fine £30/$55

FAUSTINA II - Wife of Marcus Aurelius.
Made Augusta 147 AD. Died - 175 AD

Period 1, Her lifetime

Obverse A	Obverse B

CRB168: Sestertius.
- **Fine £54/$97**

CRB169: Sestertii.
Allegorical types
- **Fine £36/$65**

CRB170: Dupondii and
Asses. Allegorical types
- **Fine £20/$35**

FAUSTINA II - Wife of Marcus Aurelius. (continued)

Period 2, Commemorative

Obverse C

CRB171: Sestertius - **Fine £55/$100**
(and similar types)

VERUS - 161 - 169 AD
(Co-Emperor with Marcus Aurelius)

Obverse A

Obverse B

Obverse C

Obverse D

CRB173: Dupondii (radiate bust) and Asses - **Fine £36/$65**
(various types)

CRB172: Sestertius - **Fine £60/$110**
(and similar allegorical and military types)

CRB174: Commemorative Sestertius - **Fine £70/$125**
(reverse as CRB166)

LUCILLA - Wife of Verus from 164 AD. Died 183 AD

Obverse A

Obverse B

CRB175: Sestertii. Alegorical types - **Fine £55/$100**

CRB176: Dupondii and Asses. Allegorical types - **Fine £24/$43**

COMMODUS - 177 - 192 AD
(son of Marcus Aurelius)

Period 1, as Caesar 175 - 177 AD

CRB177: Sestertii.
Allegorical types -
Fine £70/$125

CRB178: Dupondii
and Asses -
Fine £30/$55

Obverse A

Period 2, as Augustus

By this reign the Sestertius has often lost its roundness and the flan can be almost square. Though listed at a higher price than the Dupondius and the As, the Sestertius of this period is the most common base metal denomination.

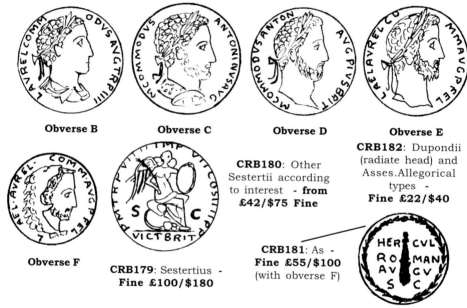

Obverse B   Obverse C   Obverse D   Obverse E

CRB180: Other
Sestertii according
to interest - **from
£42/$75 Fine**

CRB182: Dupondii
(radiate head) and
Asses.Allegorical
types -
Fine £22/$40

Obverse F

CRB179: Sestertius -
Fine £100/$180

CRB181: As -
Fine £55/$100
(with obverse F)

CRISPINA - Wife of Commodus from 178 AD. Died - c 183 AD

CRB183: Sestertii. Allegorical
types - **Fine £60/$110**

CRB184: Dupondii and Asses.
Allegorical types -
Fine £30/$55

Obverse A   Obverse B

PERTINAX - 193 AD
Murdered after reigning 86 days

CRB185: Sestertii.
Allegorical types - **Fine**
£600/$1080 at least

CRB186: Dupondii
(radiate bust) and Asses.
Allegorical types - **Fine**
£300/$540 at least

DIDIUS JULIANUS - 193 AD
Beheaded after reigning 66 days

CRB187: Sestertii and
Dupondii (radiate bust) -
Fine £300/$540 at least

CLODIUS ALBINUS - 193 - 195 AD
Caesar under Septimius Severus

CRB188: Sestertii.
Allegorical types -
Fine £145/$260

CRB189:Asses.
Allegorical types -
Fine £70/$125

SEPTIMIUS SEVERUS - 193 - 211 AD

Obverse A

Obverse B

Obverse C

CRB190: Sestertius
- **Fine £215/$385**

Obverse D

CRB191: Sestertii.
Allegorical, imperial and
military types
- **From £65/$115 Fine**
(according to interest)

CRB192: Dupondii
(radiate bust) and Asses.
Allegorical, imperial and
military types
- **From £33/$60 Fine**

SEPTIMIUS SEVERUS - 193 - 211 AD

CRB193: Commemorative Sestertii.
- **Fine £180/$325**

JULIA DOMNA - Wife of Septimius Severus. Died - 217 AD

Obverse A   **Obverse B**   **Obverse C**

CRB195: Sestertii.
Allegorical types
- **Fine £60/$110**

CRB196: Dupondii and Asses.
Allegorical, imperial and military
types - **Fine £35/$63**

CRB194: Sestertius
- **Fine £70/$125**
(the goddess Cybele
enthroned)

CARACALLA - 198 - 217 AD
(Confusingly, he is ANTONINUS PIUS on his coins)

Period 1, as Caesar 195 - 198 AD

CRB197: Sestertii.
Allegorical types
- **Fine £80/$145**

CRB198: As -
Fine £35/$63

Obverse A   **Obverse B**

Period 2, as Augustus

Obverse C   **Obverse D**   **Obverse E**   **Obverse F**

CARACALLA - 198 - 217 AD

Obverse G

CRB199: Sestertii. Usual types - **Fine £60/$110** (there are rare varieties, such as that showing the Circus Maximus in Rome)

CRB200: Dupondii (radiate head) and Asses. Usual types - **Fine £33/$60**

PLAUTILLA - Wife of Caracalla from 202 AD. Banished 205 AD, died - 211 AD

CRB202: Asses. Allegorical types - **Fine £95/$170**

GETA - 209 - 212 AD
Younger son of Septimius Severus

Period 1, as Caesar 198 - 209 AD

Obverse A

Obverse B

CRB203: Sestertius - **Fine £70/$125**

CRB204: Dupondii and Ass es - **From £48/$85 Fine**

Period 2, as Augustus

Obverse C

Obverse D

CRB205: Sestertii. Usual types - **Fine £85/$155** (less usual types more expensive)

CRB206: Dupondii (radiate head) and Asses - **Fine £48/$85**

MACRINUS - 212 - 218 AD

CRB207: Sestertii.
Allegorical types
- **Fine £170/$305**

CRB208: Dupondii
(radiate head) and Asses
- **Fine £55/$100**

DIADUMENIAN
Son of Macrinus, Caesar 217 - 218 AD

CRB209: Sestertius. Main type, as illustration
- **Fine £240/$430**

CRB210: Dupondius and As -
Fine £90/$160
(both bare headed, reverse as illustration)

ELAGABALUS - 218 - 222 AD
Priest of the Syrian sun god. Assassinated aged 17.

Another ANTONINVS PIVS, easily confused with Caracalla; but Elagabalus' legends begin IMP, or read ANTONINVS PIVS FEL AVG.

CRB215: Sestertii.
Allegorical, emperor
sacrificing -
Fine £90/$160

CRB216: Dupondii
(radiate head)
and Asses -
Fine £40/$72
(as illustration and
allegorical types)

JULIA PAULA
First wife of Elagabalus 219 - 220 AD

CRB217:
Dupondii and
Asses. Usual types
- **Fine £95/$170**

AQUILIA SEVERA
Second wife of Elagabalus 220 - 222 AD

CRB218:
Dupondii and
Asses. Allegorical
types -
Fine £120/$215

JULIA SOAEMIAS
Mother of Elagabalus. Died 222 AD

CRB219: Sestertii.
Usual types
- **Fine £145/$260**

CRB220: Dupondii
and Asses
- **Fine £60/$110**

JULIA MAESA
Sister of Julia Domna, Grandmother of
Elagabalus and Severus Alexander

CRB221: Sestertii.
Usual types
- **Fine £90/$160**

CRB222: Dupondii
and Asses
- **Fine £42/$75**

SEVERUS ALEXANDER - 222 - 235 AD

Period 1, as Caesar 221 - 222 AD

Obverse A

CRB223: Sestertius.
Sacrificial implements.
Similar to CRB178
- **Fine £190/$340**

CRB224: As. Reverse
as CRB210 -
Fine £110/$200

Period 2, as Augustus

Obverse B

Obverse C

Obverse D

CRB227:
Dupondii (radiate
head) and Asses.
Allegorical types -
Fine £18/$32

CRB225: Sestertius. Sol
standing, and similar
types
- **Fine £24/$43**

CRB226: As -
Fine £36/$65

ORBIANA
Married Severus Alexander 225 AD

CRB228: Sestertius. Fig.7
reverse with legend:
CONCORDIA
AVGVSTORVM
Fine £200/$360

CRB229: As.
Reverse as CRB228
- **Fine £18/$32**

JULIA MAMAEA
Mother of Severus Alexander - Died 235 AD

CRB230: Sestertii.
Allegorical types
- **Fine £36/$65**

CRB231: Dupondii
and Asses.
Allegorical types
- **Fine £33/$60**

MAXIMINUS I - 235 - 238 AD
The Thracian

CRB232: Sestertii. Allegorical types - **Fine £30/$55**

CRB233: Dupondii (radiate bust) and **CRB234**: Asses. Allegorical types - **Fine £22/$40 each**

MAXIMUS I
Son of Maximinus, Caesar 235 - 238 AD

CRB235: Sestertii. Allegorical types - **Fine £48/$85**

CRB236: Dupondii and Asses. Allegorical types - **Fine £42/$75**

BALBINUS 238 AD
Reigned 98 days. Assassinated by the Praetorian guard.

CRB237: Sestertii. Usual types - **Fine £120/$215**

PUPIENUS 238 AD
Joint Emperor with Balbinus. Shared his fate.

CRB238: Sestertii. Usual types - **Fine £120/$215**

GORDIAN III 238 - 244 AD

Period 1, as Caesar, 238 AD under Balbinus and Pupienus

Obverse A

CRB239:
Sestertius - **Fine**
£120/$215

Period 2, as Augustus

Obverse B Obverse C

CRB240: Sestertii. Allegorical types
- **Fine £24/$43**
(other types dearer according to interest)

PHILIP I - 244 - 249 AD
The Arabian

During this reign, in 248 AD, Rome celebrated its 1000 year anniversary. Coins with the legend SAECULARES AVGG commemorate this event.

CRB243: Sestertii with animal reverses - **Fine £36/$65**

CRB244: Sestertii. Allegorical types - **Fine £24/$43**

CRB245: Dupondius (radiate head) - **Fine £30/$55**

CRB246: Dupondii and Asses. Allegorical types - **Fine £18/$32 each**

OCTACILIA SEVERA - Wife of Philip I

During this reign a crescent at the shoulders distinguishes, for the first time, the Dupondius from the As in the case of females.

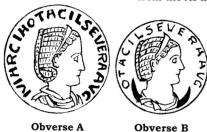

Obverse A　　**Obverse B**

CRB247: Sestertii. Animal types -
　　Fine £42/$75

CRB248: Sestertii. Allegorical types -
　　Fine £30/$55

CRB249: Dupondii (with crescent at shoulders on obverse) and Asses -
　　Fine £22/$40

PHILIP II - Shared rule 247 - 249 AD
Son of Philip I

Note that Philip I and Philip II use the same obverse legends but, unless the coin is well-worn, they can be distinguished by the youthfulness of Philip II's portrait.

Period 1, as Caesar, 244 - 247 AD

CRB251: Dupondii and Asses -
　　Fine £22/$40

CRB250: Sestertius -
　　Fine £36/$65

Period 2, as Augustus 247 - 249 AD

Obverse B　　**Obverse C**

CRB252: Sestertius -
　　Fine £42/$75
(reverse shows Philip I and Philip II enthroned)

CRB253: Sestertii. Animal types -
Fine £42/$75

CRB254: Sestertii. Allegorical types
- **Fine £28/$50**

CRB255: Dupondii (radiate head) and Asses. Allegorical types
- **Fine £22/$40**

TRAJAN DECIUS - 249 - 251 AD

Obverse A   **Obverse B**   **Obverse C**

CRB256: Double Sestertius -
Fine £180/$325
(Obverse A with reverse
legend FELICITAS SAECVLI)

CRB260: Semis -
Fine £24/$43

CRB257: Sestertius -
Fine £36/$65
(Obverse B, reverse shows
figures representing the two
provinces of Pannonia)

CRB258: Sestertii.
Allegorical types
- **Fine £30/$55**

CRB259: Dupondii
(radiate head) and Asses
- **Fine £24/$43**

HERENNIA ETRUSCILLA - Wife of Trajan Decius

Obverse A   **Obverse B**

CRB261: Sestertii. Allegorical types
- **Fine £36/$65**

CRB262: Dupondius (Obv B). Fig.27 reverse with
legend: PVDICITIA AVG
- **Fine £30/$55**

CRB263: As (Obv A but smaller). Reverse as CRB262
- **Fine £30/$55**

HERENNIUS ETRUSCUS - Elder Son of Trajan Decius

Caesar 250 - 251 AD. Augustus for about a month, during which time no base metal coins
were issued in his name.

CRB264: Sestertius. Reverse types as Figs.24 or 26
- **Fine £60/$110**

CRB265: Dupondius or As. Reverse types also as
Figs.24 or 26 - **Fine £54/$97**

HOSTILIAN - 251 AD
Younger son of Trajan Decius

Period 1, as Caesar December 250 - July 251 AD

CRB266: Sestertius. Reverse types as Figs.24 or 26
- **Fine £85/$155**

CRB267: Dupondius or As. Reverse types also as
Figs.24 or 26 - **Fine £60/$110**

Period 2, As Augustus. Proclaimed by Trebonianus Gallus in July 251 AD. Died of Plague circa November 251 AD.

CRB268: Sestertii. Allegorical types -
Fine £110/$200

CRB269: As. Reverse as Fig.23 with legend: PIETAS
AVGVST - **Fine £84/$150**

TREBONIANUS GALLUS - 251 - 253 AD

CRB270: Sestertius -
Fine £72/$130
(Illustrated right)

CRB271: Sestertii.
Allegorical types -
Fine £30/$55

Obverse A   **Obverse B**

CRB272: Asses. Allegorical
types - **Fine £30/$55**

VOLUSIAN - 251 - 253 AD

Period 1, as Caesar July - November 251 AD

CRB273: Sestertius -
Reverse similar to
Fig.26 with legend:
PRINCIPI IVVENTVTIS -
Fine £110/$200

CRB274: Dupondii and
Asses - Reverse similar
to Fig.22 with legend:
PAX AVGG -
Fine £84/$150

VOLUSIAN - 251 - 253 AD (Continued)

Period 2, as Augustus

CRB275: Sestertius -
Reverse as CRB270
- **Fine £72/$130**

CRB276: Sestertii.
Allegorical types -
Fine £36/$65

CRB277: Dupondius
(radiate head). With
reverse legend:
CONCORDIA AVGG
- **Fine £72/$130**

CRB278: Asses.
Allegorical types -
Fine £30/$55

AEMILIAN - 253 AD
A rebel who reigned about 3 months.

CRB279: Sestertii.
Reverse similar to
Fig.37 with legend:
VIRTVS AVGG
- **Fine £275/$495
at least**

CRB280: As. Reverse
similar to Fig.32 with
legend: SPES PVBLICA
- **Fine £215/$385**

VALERIAN I - 253 - 260 AD

CRB281: Sestertii. Allegorical types -
Fine £48/$85

CRB282:Dupondii (radiate head). Allegorical types
- **Fine £37/$67**

CRB283: Asses. Allegorical types -
Fine £30/$55

VALERIAN II - 255/6 - 258 AD
Son of Gallienus

CRB284: As. Reverse
similar to Fig.24 with
legend: PRINCIPI
IVVENT -
Fine £110/$200

CRB285: Dupondius
(commemorative).
Reverse similar to
CRB171 with legend:
CONSECRATIO
- **Fine £120/$215**

CRB286: As (commemorative).
Reverse similar to CRB153
- **Fine £120/$215**

SALONINUS - 258 - 260 AD
Son of Gallienus. Caesar 258 - 260. Augustus 260 AD.

CRB287: As. Reverse similar to Fig.26 with legend: PRINCIPI IVVENTVTVS - **Fine £112/$200** (issued while Saloninus was Caesar)

No base metal coins were issued during his short period as Augustus, which lasted several weeks in 260 AD.

GALLIENUS - 253 - 268 AD
Son of Valerian I and co-Emperor until 260 AD.

Part 1, the 'traditional' bronze coins

CRB288: Sestertii. Allegorical types - **Fine £48/$85**

CRB289: Dupondii (radiate head). Allegorical types - **Fine £65/$115**

CRB290: Asses. Allegorical types - **Fine £42/$75**

Obverse A   Obverse B

PHASE THREE - THE RADIATE PERIOD

Around 258 AD, the silver content of the Double-Denarius (the 'Antoninianus') was so much reduced that it became virtually a bronze coin. For convenience I count the change over of this denomination from silver to bronze, as 260 AD. As far as this book is concerned the Antoniniani of Valerian are silver (and so not included in this book), whilst those of Gallienus and Salonina are bronze, despite the fact some of their coins were minted before the debasement and are in fact base silver.

GALLIENUS, Part 2, the Antoniniani

From this point onwards Sestertii, Dupondii and Asses are rarely minted, and unless otherwise stated all coins catalogued are Antoniniani. Due to the precious metal content of the coins (although minimal) the letters 'S.C' no longer appear on the base metal coins except where occasionally the old denominations occur. Note that well-silvered coins can be worth around three times as much as non-silvered.

Obverse C   Obverse D

CRB291: Legionary types (two different reverses shown) - **Very Fine from £55/$100**

GALLIENUS, Part 2 (continued)

CRB292: Mythical being types
(two different reverses shown)
- **Very Fine from £16/$30**

CRB293: Animal types (two
different reverses shown)
- **Very Fine from £14/$25**

CRB294: Allegorical types - **Very Fine £12/$22**

See also CRB325 and CRB326 - Anonymous coins attributed to 268 AD.

SALONINA
Wife of Gallenius - Died 268 AD.

Part 1, the 'traditional' bronze coins

CRB295: Sestertii. Allegorical
types - **Fine £60/$110**

CRB296: Dupondii (crescent at
shoulder) and Asses. Allegorical
types - **Fine £35/$63**

Part 2, the Antoniniani

CRB297: Animal types -
Very Fine £18/$32

CRB298: Allegorical types -
Very Fine £17/$30

MACRIANUS - 260 - 261 AD
Challenged the rule of Gallienus.

QUIETUS - 260 - 261 AD
Younger brother of Macrianus.

CRB299: Allegorical types
- **Very Fine £90/$160**

CRB300: Allegorical types
- **Very Fine £95/$170**

CLAUDIUS II GOTHICUS - 268 - 270 AD

Period 1, His Lifetime

CRB301: Allegorical types -
VF £12/$22
(with obverse A or B)

CRB302: As (obverse C). Reverse as
Fig.14 with legend: IOVI VICTORI -
VF £90/$160

Obverse A   Obverse B   Obverse C

Period 2, Contemporary commemorative, circa 270 AD

CRB305: Obverse D with
Allegorical type reverses -
VF £33/$60

CRB306: Barbaric copies of
CRB304 - **VF £10/$18**

Obverse D   CRB303 -   CRB304 -
        VF £14/$25   VF £14/$25

Later Commemorative, circa 317 - 318 AD
(Constantine claimed Claudius as an ancestor!)

Obverse E   CRB307 -   CRB308 -   CRB309 -
       VF £33/$60   VF £33/$60   VF £33/$60

QUINTILLUS - January - April of 270 AD
Younger brother of Claudius II

CRB310: Allegorical types -
VF £22/$40 - £28/$50

Obverse A   Obverse B

THE BREAKAWAY ROMANO-GALLIC EMPIRE 260 - 274 AD

POSTUMUS - 260 - 274 AD

Older denominations

Obverse A

CRB311: Double Sestertius
- **Fine £90/$160**
(with obverse A)

CRB312: Double Sestertius
- **Fine £58/$105**

The Antoniniani (remember that well-silvered coins are worth more)

Obverse B

CRB313: Featuring the River Rhine seated
- **VF £35/$63**

CRB314: Allegorical types
- **VF £15/$27**

LAELIANUS - Circa 4 months of 269 AD

Rebelled against Postumus, and reigned in lower Germany.

CRB315: Reverse as Fig.36 with legend:
VICTORIA AVG -
VF £390/$700

MARIUS - 269 AD

Probably reigned only two months.

Obverse A

Obverse B

CRB316: Allegorical types
- **VF £80/$145**

46

VICTORINUS - 269 - early 271 AD

CRB317: Allegorical types
- **VF £12/$22**

Obverse A   Obverse B

TETRICUS I - 271 - 274 AD

CRB318: Allegorical types
- **VF £10/$18**

CRB318A: Barbarous
copies of Tetricus coins
- **VF £10/$18**

Obverse A   Obverse B

TETRICUS II Caesar - 273 - 274 AD
Son of Tetricus I

CRB319: Allegorical types
- **VF £14/$25**

THE END OF THE BREAKAWAY ROMANO - GALLIC EMPIRE

In 274 the Romano-Gallic Empire came back into the mainstream Roman Empire, the Tetrici being allowed to retire into private life.

AURELIAN - 270 - 275 AD

During this reign a reform of the coinage took place and, from now until early in Diocletian's reign, many of the coins have XXI in the exergue of the reverse (probably meaning that the coin is composed of twenty parts copper to one part silver).

Obverse A   Obverse B   Obverse C

CRB320: Two-figure types -
VF £17/$30
(with obverse A or B)

AURELIAN - 270 - 275 AD (Continued)

CRB322: Dupondius or As. Two figure type reverse with legend: CONCORDIA AVG
- **Fine £38/$68**
(with obverse C)

CRB321: Allegorical types
- **VF £17/$30**
(with obverse A or B)

SEVERINA

Wife of Aurelian. Minted coins from 274 during Aurelian's reign, then during the six month's Interregnum when she ruled the empire.

CRB323: Allegorical and two-figure types - **VF £33/$60**

CRB324: As (obverse has no crescent - thicker coin) Allegorical types - **Fine £38/$68**

ANONYMOUS COINS OF THE PERIOD

Now attributed to 268 AD during the reign of Gallienus.

CRB326: Dupondius. Smaller version of CRB325 - **Fine £105/$190**

CRB325: Sestertius - **Fine £180/$325**

The "Mushroom" Empire of PALMYRA

A city in the Syrian desert and its surrounding area. When Queen Zenobia of Palmyra dared to call her son Emperor, the Romans under Aurelian marched and conquered the city in 272 AD.

VABALATHUS

Son of Queen Zenobia.

CRB327A: Independent ruler. Reverse legend: VICTORIA AVG. Very rare
- **VF £550/$990 at least**

CRB327: As a 'colleague' of Aurelian
- **VF £25/$45**
(head on both obverse and reverse)

48

TACITUS - September 275 - April 276 AD
Elected by the senate.

Obverse A   **Obverse B**

CRB329: As (laureate
bust and thicker flan)
Fig.18 reverse with
legend: MARS VLTOR -
Fine £88/$160

CRB328: Allegorical and two-
figure types - **VF £22/$40**
(with obverse A or B)

FLORIAN - April - June 276 AD
Half-brother of Tacitus.

CRB330: Allegorical types
- **VF £65/$115**

Obverse A   **Obverse B**

PROBUS - 276 - 282 AD

Obverse A   **Obverse B**   **Obverse C**   **Obverse D**

Obverse E   **Obverse F**   **CRB331**:   **CRB332**:
                        - **VF £20/$35**   - **VF £20/$35**

CRB333: Allegorical and two
figure types according to interest
- **VF from £17/$30**

CARUS - 282 - 283 AD

Period 1, his Lifetime

CRB334: Allegorical and two-figure types - **VF £38/$68**

Obverse A   Obverse B

Period 2, Commemorative

CRB336: Altar similar to CRB304 - **VF £38/$68**

Obverse C   Obverse D   CRB335:
- **VF £28/$50**

CARINUS - 283 - 285 AD

Period 1, as Caesar 282 - 283 AD

CRB337: Allegorical and two-figure types - **VF £33/$60** (with obverse A)

CRB338: Denarius (Half-Antoninianus) - **VF £130/$235** (with obverse B)

Obverse A   Obverse B

Period 2, as Augustus

CRB339: Mainly allegorical types - **VF £33/$60**

Obverse C   Obverse D

MAGNIA URBICA
Wife of Carinus

CRB340: With reverse legend: VENVS VICTRIX - **VF £165/$295**

CRB340A: With reverse legend: VENVS GENETRIX - **VF £165/$295**

NUMERIAN - 283 - 284 AD
Brother of Carinus

Obverse A　　　**Obverse B**　　　**Obverse C**　　　**Obverse D**

CRB341: Allegorical and two-
figure types - **VF £33/$60**
(Numerian as Ceasar, obverse A)

CRB342: Similar to CRB341 -
VF £28/$50
(Numerian as Augustus, obverses B and C)

CRB343: Commemorative eagle and altar
types, as CRB335 and CRB336 -
VF £33/$60
(DIVO/divine, obverse D)

THE BREAKAWAY BRITISH EMPIRE

CARAUSIUS - 287 - 293 AD

Obverse A　　　**Obverse B**　　　**CRB344**: Legion types　　　**CRB345**: Allegorical
- **VF £145/$260**　　　types - **VF £30/$55**

CRB345A: Barbarous local copies - **VF £18/$32**

ALLECTUS - 293 - 296 AD
Chief minister of Carausius, whom he murdered.

CRB346: Allegorical
types - **VF £42/$75**

CRB347: Quinarius -
VF £24/$43

END OF THE BREAKAWAY BRITISH EMPIRE
Constantius I invaded Britain and recovered the province for the Empire in 296 AD.

PHASE FOUR - COLLEAGUES IN EMPIRE

Diocletian devised a system of rule whereby two Augusti divided the Roman Empire between them, each having an assistant Emperor (a Caesar) to help him and, in time, to succeed to the full power. From now on all mints normally coin in the names of all reigning Augusti and Caesars.

Mint towns are beginning to place their mint initials on the reverse of the coinage. As London minted coins between the reigns of Carausius and 325 AD, we now have the London Mint factor affecting pricing. London coins tend to be more sought after (especially in the UK) than coins from other cities, and are therefore more expensive than similar coins from other mints. For a list of mint towns and the letters they used, see appendix II on page 76. In 294 AD Diocletian reformed the coinage, introducing the Follis as the new, main denomination.

Note that from now on, rulers (with exceptions like Julian II Augustus) can no longer be recognised by their portraits. A ruler can look entirely different from one coin to the next.

DIOCLETIAN - 284 - 305 AD

Period 1, before the 294 AD reform (all Antoniniani)

Obverse A

Obverse B

CRB348: Two-figure Eastern mint types (2 reverse types shown) - **VF £14/$25** (obverse A)

CRB349: Allegorical types from Rome and other central mints - **VF £14/$25**

CRB350: Allegorical types without the XXI. Lugdunum mint - **VF £14/$25**

CRB351: Allegorical 'AUGGG' types - **VF £95/$170** (obverse B, and minted by Carausius)

Period 2, after 294 AD (Folles and Fractional Folles)

Note that all of the types listed were minted in the names of all the rulers of the period!

Obverse C

Obverse D

CRB352: Follis - **VF £22/$40** (the basic type for this period)

Period 2, after 294 AD (continued)

CRB353: Follis - VF £24/$43

CRB354: Follis - VF £26/$47 (minted only in Carthage)

CRB355: Follis - VF £26/$47 (minted only in Carthage)

 CRB356: No XXI in the exergue. This is known as a 'Post-reform Radiate' or a 'Fractional Follis' - **VF £14/$25** (obverse A)

CRB357: Fracional Follis - VF £16/$30 (obverse A)

Period 3, after his abdication in 305 AD

Obverse E

Obverse F

CRB358: Follis - VF £38/$68 (obverse E)

CRB359: Follis - VF £38/$68 (obverse F)

MAXIMIANUS - 286 - 305 AD

With a second reign 306 - 308 AD and a very short third reign in 310 AD, in which year he died

Period 1, before 294 AD reform (all Antoniniani)

Note that reverse are exactly in line with those of Diocletian.

Obverse A

Obverse B

Obverse C

CRB360: as CRB348 - **VF £14/$25**
CRB361: as CRB349 - **VF £14/$25**
CRB362: as CRB350 - **VF £14/$25**
CRB363: as CRB351 - **VF £95/$170**

MAXIMIANUS - 286 - 305 AD

Period 2, after 294 AD reform (Folles and Fractional Folles)

Obverse D **Obverse E** **Obverse F**

The Folles

CRB364: as CRB352 -
VF £22/$40
CRB365: as CRB353 -
VF £20/$35
CRB366: as CRB354 -
VF £22/$40
CRB367: as CRB355 -
VF £22/$40

CRB368: Fractional Follis as CRB356 -
VF £12/$22 (with obverse A, B or C)
CRB369: Fractional Follis as CRB357 -
VF £14/$25 (with obverse A, B or C)
CRB370: Quarter Follis from Siscia mint 305-306 AD -
VF £14/$25 (with obverse F)

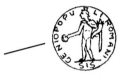

CRB371: as CRB358.
Struck after the abdica-
tion of 305 AD -
VF £33/$60

CRB372: Follis, from the
second reign 306 - 308
AD - **VF £17/$30**

Period 3, Commemorative

Struck 310 - 311 AD under Maxentius

Struck 317 - 318 AD under Constantine I

CRB373: Follis -
VF £33/$60

CRB374: Quarter Follis
- **VF £22/$40**

CRB375: Quarter Follis. Obverse as
CRB374. Two reverse types shown.
Both types - **VF £22/$40 each**

CONSTANTIUS I

Caesar 293 - 305 AD. Augustus 305 - 306 AD

Period 1, as Caesar, before 294 AD reform (all Antoniniani)

CRB376: Two-figure types, XXI in exergue as CRB348 - **VF £22/$40**

CRB377: Similar to CRB350 - **VF £22/$40**

Obverse A   Obverse B

Period 2, as Caesar, after 294 AD (Folles and Fractional Folles)

Reverses in line with those of Diocletian and Maximian

CRB378: as CRB352 - **VF £20/$35**
CRB379: as CRB353 - **VF £20/$35**
CRB380: as CRB354 - **VF £22/$40**
CRB381: as CRB355 - **VF £22/$40**

Obverse C   Obverse D

CRB383: Fractional Follis as CRB356 - **VF £14/$25** (obverse A)

CRB384: Fractional Follis as CRB357 - **VF £14/$25** (obverse A)

CRB382: - **VF £24/$43**

Period 3, as Augustus

CRB385: as CRB352 - **VF £28/$50** (with obverse E)

CRB386: as CRB356 - **VF £26/$47** (with obverse F)

CRB387: as CRB370 - **VF £22/$40** (with obverse G)

Obverse E   Obverse F   Obverse G

CONSTANTIUS I (continued)

Period 5, Commemorative

| Obverse H | Obverse I | CRB388: -
VF £44/$80 | CRB389: -
VF £38/$68 |

CRB390: as CRB374 - **VF £33/$60**

CRB391: as CRB375 - **VF £33/$60**   **CRB392**: as CRB375 - **VF £33/$60**
(bird reverse)   (beast reverse)

GALERIUS
Caesar 293 - 305 AD. Augustus 305 - 311 AD
Unfortunately, another Maximianus on his coins!

Period 1, as Caesar, before 294 AD reform (all Antoniniani)

CRB393: Two-figure types with XXI in exergue.
Similar to CRB348 - **VF £20/$35**

CRB394: Similar to CRB350 - **VF £20/$35**

Obverse A   Obverse B

Period 2, as Caesar, after 294 AD (Folles and Fractional Folles)

Reverses in line with those of Diocletian,
Maximian and Constantine.

Double-check that your coin reads
MAXIMIANVS and not MAXIMINVS.

Obverse C   Obverse D

CRB395: as CRB352 - **VF £24/$43**
CRB396: as CRB353 - **VF £26/$47**
CRB397: as CRB354 - **VF £28/$50**
CRB398: as CRB355 - **VF £30/$55**
CRB399: as CRB382 - **VF £28/$50**
CRB400: Fractional Follis, as CRB356 - **VF £20/$35**
(with obverse A or B)
CRB401: Fractional Follis, similar to CRB357 - **VF £22/$40**
(with obverse A or B)

GALERIUS (continued)

Period 3, as Augustus 305 - 311 AD

(all are Folles or Fractional Folles)

| Obverse E | Obverse F | Obverse G | Obverse H |

Note that obverse G is more or less the same as a Maximian obverse. If the reverse is the 'GENIO POPVLI ROMANI type, it can only be Maximian.

CRB402: GENIO POPVLI ROMANI type (as CRB352). With either obverse E or F - **VF £22/$40**

CRB406: Fractional Follis, as CRB356 - **VF £18/$32** (with obverse H)

CRB404: - VF £18/$32   CRB405: - VF £18/$32

GALERIA VALERIA

Daughter of Diocletian, wife of Galerius - died c315 AD.

CRB407: Follis - **VF £60/$110**

SEVERUS II

Caesar 305 - 306 AD - Augustus 306 - 307 AD.

| Obverse A | Obverse B | Obverse C | Obverse D |

SEVERUS II (continued)

Period 1, as Caesar (obverses A - D)

CRB408: as CRB352 - **VF £60/$110**
CRB409: as CRB382 - **VF £60/$110**
CRB410: as CRB353 - **VF £65/$115**

CRB411: as CRB355 - **VF £70/$125**
CRB412: Fractional Follis, as CRB356 -
VF £55/$100 (with obverse C)
CRB413: Quarter-Follis as CRB370 -
VF £55/$100 (with obverse D)

Period 2, as Augustus

Obverse E   Obverse F   Obverse G

CRB414: -
VF £70/$125

CRB415: -
VF £82/$150

CRB416: Fractional Follis, as CRB356 - **VF £55/$100**
(with obverse G)

MAXIMINUS II Daia
Caesar 305 - 310 AD - Augustus 310 - 313 AD.
Beware: Maximinus can be easily misread as Maximianus.

Period 1, as Caesar

Obverse A   Obverse B   Obverse C   Obverse D

CRB417: as CRB352 - **VF £22/$40**

CRB418: as CRB353 - **VF £28/$50**

CRB419: as CRB355 - **VF £33/$50**

CRB420: as CRB382 - **VF £30/$55**

MAXIMINUS II Daia (continued)

CRB423: Fractional Follis, as
CRB356 - **VF £24/$43**
(with obverse D)

CRB421: - **VF £20/$35**   **CRB422**: - **VF £30/$55**

Period 2, as Augustus

Note that by now the Follis had become a much smaller coin.

CRB425: GENIO
AVGVSTI, as CRB405
- **VF £16/$30**

Obverse E   Obverse F

CRB426: - **VF £16/$30**

CRB427: -
VF £16/$30

CRB428: -
VF £26/$47

CRB429: -
VF £18/$32

CRB430: - **VF £12/$22**

Anonymous Quarter-Folles

Minted 310 - 313 in Antioch.

CRB431: - **VF £20/$35**   **CRB432**: - **VF £26/$47**

59

MAXENTIUS - 306 - 312 AD
Son of Maximian

Obverse A   **Obverse B**   **Obverse C**   **Obverse D**

CRB433: -
VF £22/$40

CRB434: -
VF £24/$43

CRB435: -
VF £24/$43

CRB436: -
VF £28/$50

   CRB437: Half Follis
- **VF £28/$50**

   CRB438: Third Follis
- **VF £26/$47**
(obverse D)

ROMULUS - 306 - 312 AD
Son of Maxentius - died 309 AD. Commemorative coins.

CRB439: Temple reverse as
CRB388 - **VF £165/$295**
(obverse A)

CRB440: Quarter Follis similar
to CRB439 - **VF £70/$125**
(obverse B)

Obverse A   **Obverse B**

Up till now the larger bronze coins could reasonably be called Folles; but from now on no attempt is made to name the denomination.

60

LICINIUS I - 308 - 324 AD

Obverses:

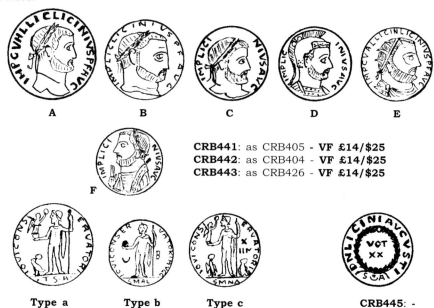

A   B   C   D   E

F

CRB441: as CRB405 - **VF £14/$25**
CRB442: as CRB404 - **VF £14/$25**
CRB443: as CRB426 - **VF £14/$25**

Type a	Type b	Type c	CRB445: -

CRB444: IOVI CONSERVATORI types, 3 of which shown
    - **VF £12/$22 each**

CRB445: -
VF £12/$22

CRB446: -
VF £12/$22

CRB447: -
VF £33/$60

CRB447A: "Constantinian"
types as CRB459, CRB463,
CRB464 and CRB465 (from
the territories Constantine
controlled) naming LICINIUS
on the obverse - **Prices as for
Constantine**

LICINIUS II

Caesar 317 - 324 AD. Son of Licinius I

Obverse A   Obverse B   Obverse C

CRB448: IOVI CONSERVATORI types, as CRB444 a and b - **VF £14/$25 each**

CRB449: Gateway type, as CRB446 - **VF £14/$25**

CRB450: Similar to CRB445 - **VF £14/$25**

CONSTANTINE I, the Great

Caesar 306 - 307 AD. Augustus 307 - 337 AD.
See also commemoratives for Claudius - CRB308 and CRB309, and Maximianus
- CRB374 and CRB 375.

Period 1, as Caesar

CRB451: as CRB352 - **VF £32/$58**

CRB452: as CRB356 - **VF £24/$43**
(with Obverse B)

Obverse A   **Obverse B**

Period 2, as Augustus (shared rule until 324 AD: sole rule after 324 AD)

Obverses:

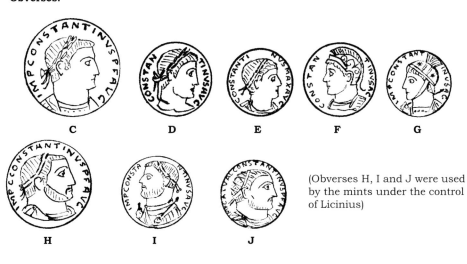

C   D   E   F   G

H   I   J

(Obverses H, I and J were used
by the mints under the control
of Licinius)

CRB453: as CRB405 - **VF £12/$22**

CRB454: as CRB426 - **VF £13/$23**

CRB455: IOVI CONSERVATORI
types, as CRB444 a, b and c
- **VF £12/$22 each**

CRB456: -   **CRB457**: -
VF **£24/$43**   VF **£22/$40**

CONSTANTINE I, the Great (continued)

CRB458: -
VF £24/$43

CRB459: -
VF £26/$47

CRB460: -
VF £28/$50

CRB461: -
VF £30/$55

CRB462: -
VF £18/$32

CRB463: -
VF £16/$30

CRB464: -
VF £18/$32

CRB465: -
VF £16/$30

CRB466: And similar
'VOT' coins -
VF £11/$20

CRB467: -
VF £11/$20

CRB468: -
VF £17/$30

Minted after 324 AD:

CRB469: -
VF £11/$20

CRB470: -
VF £12/$22

CRB471: -
VF £38/$68

CRB472: -
VF £8/$15

CRB473: This type was minted 335 -
341 AD by both Constantine I and
Constantine II - using the same
obverse legend. A fuller catalogue is
needed to distinguish them! -
VF £8/$15

CRB474: As
last, but with
Christogram on
the standard
- VF £10/$18

Period 3, Commemorative

Obverse K

CRB475: -
VF £16/$30

CRB476: -
VF £16/$30

CRB477: -
VF £16/$30

CRISPUS

Caesar 317 - 326 AD. Eldest son of Constantine.

Obverses:

| A | B | C | D | E |

CRB478: Reverse:
VICTORIAE LAETAE.., as
CRB464 - **VF £20/$35**

CRB479: Reverse:
VIRTVS EXERCIT, as
CRB465 - **VF £18/$32**

CRB480: Reverse:
BEATA TRANQLITAS, as
CRB467 - **VF £16/$30**

Note that
Obverse E was
used at mints
controlled by
Licinius.

CRB482: -
VF £22/$40

CRB483: -
VF £16/$30

CRB484: -
VF £14/$25

CONSTANTINE II

Caesar 317 - 337 AD. Augustus 337 - 340 AD

Period 1, as Caesar

Obverses: (D and E were used at mints controlled by Licinius)

| A | B | C | D | E |

CRB485: Reverse: IOVI
CONS.. as CRB444 b and c
- **VF £20/$35**

CRB486: Reverse:
VIRTVS EXERCIT, as
CRB465 - **VF £16/$30**

CRB487: as CRB483
- **VF £11/$20**

CRB488: Reverse:
BEATA TRANQLITAS, as
CRB467 - **VF £11/$20**

CRB489: as CRB484
- **VF £11/$20**

CRB490: Reverse:
GLORIA EXERCITVS, as
CRB472 (2 standards)
- **VF £8/$15**

CRB491: Reverse:
GLORIA EXERCITVS, as
CRB473 (1 standard)
- **VF £5/$10**

CRB492: -
VF £17/$30

CRB493: -
VF £16/$30

CRB494: -
VF £16/$30

CONSTANTINE II (continued)

Period 2, as Augustus

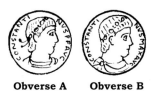

Obverse A   **Obverse B**

CRB495: GLORIA EXERCITVS, as CRB473. See also note for CRB473
- **VF £18/$32**

CRB496:
VF £22/$40

FAUSTA
Married Constantine 307 AD. Died 326 AD.

CRB497: VF £36/$65   **CRB498: VF £36/$65**

HELENA
Mother of Constantine I. Died c328 AD (first wife of Constantius I)

CRB499: VF £26/$47   **CRB500: VF £20/$35**
(struck during her lifetime)   (struck after her lifetime, mnted 337 - 340 AD))

THEODORA
Second wife of Constantius I

CRB501: VF £20/$35
(struck after her lifetime, mnted 337 - 340 AD)

Anonymous Coins of the Period - 330 - 346 AD

Period 1, 330 - 335 AD or later.
Commemorating Constantinople becoming twin capital of the Roman Empire with Rome.

CRB502: Rome -
VF £10/$18

CRB503: Constantinople
- **VF £6/$10**

CRB504: Obverse of CRB502 or CRB503 with reverse legend GLORIA EXERCITVS (1 standard) -
VF £8/$15

Anonymous Coins of the Period - 330 - 346 AD

Period 2, 341 - 346 AD

CRB505: VF £17/$30

CRB506: VF £22/$40
(obverse as CRB505)

DELMATIUS
Caesar 335 - 337 AD. Nephew of Constanine I.

CRB507: Reverse: GLORIA EXERCITVS, as CRB472
(2 standards) - **VF £28/$50**

CRB508: Reverse: GLORIA EXERCITVS, as CRB473
(1 standard) - **VF £28/$50**

HANNIBALLIANUS
King of Armenia, Pontus and Cappadocia 335 - 337 AD. Nephew of Constanine I.

CRB509: Reverse: Euphrates reclining
- **VF £220/$395**

CONSTANS - 337 - 350 AD
Son of Constantine I.

Period 1, as Caesar 333 - 337 AD

CRB510: Reverse: GLORIA EXERCITVS, as CRB472
(2 standards) - **VF £8/$15**

CRB511: Reverse: GLORIA EXERCITVS, as CRB473
(1 standard) - **VF £5/$10**

Obverse A   Obverse B

Period 2, as Augustus

Obverses:

CRB512: Reverse: GLORIA
EXERCITVS, as CRB473
(1 standard) -
VF £5/$10

C   D   E   F

CONSTANS - 337 - 350 AD (continued)

CRB513: **VF £5/$10**	**CRB514:** **VF £10/$18**	**CRB515:** **VF £8/$15**	**CRB516:** 2 phoenix types - **VF £14/$25 each**

CRB517: VF £14/$25   **CRB518: VF £14/$25**   **CRB519: VF £16/$30**

CONSTANTIUS II - 337 - 361 AD
Son of Constantine I.

Period 1, as Caesar 324 - 337 AD

CRB520:as CRB 484 - **VF £9/$15**

Obverse A   **Obverse B**

CRB521: Reverse: GLORIA EXERCITVS, as CRB472
(2 standards) - **VF £5/$10**

CRB522: Reverse: GLORIA EXERCITVS, as CRB473
(1 standard) - **VF £5/$10**   **CRB523: VF £9/$15**

Period 2, as Augustus

Obverse A   **Obverse B**   **Obverse C**   **Obverse D**

CRB524: Reverse: GLORIA EXERCITVS, as CRB473 (1 standard) - **VF £8/$15**

CRB525: as CRB515 - **VF £8/$15**   **CRB527:** as CRB516 - **VF £14/$25**
CRB526: as CRB513 - **VF £8/$15**   **CRB528:** as CRB517 - **VF £14/$25**

CRB529: as CRB518 - **VF £16/$30**
CRB530: as CRB519 - **VF £18/$30**

CONSTANTIUS II (continued)

CRB531:
VF £10/$18

CRB532:
VF £12/$22

CRB532A:
VF £8/$15

CRB532B:
Barbaric
version of
CRB532
- **VF £5/$10**

CRB533:
VF £44/$80

MAGNENTIUS - 350 - 353 AD
A rebel in the West.

Obverse A

Obverse B

CRB534:
VF £24/$43

CRB535: and similar
types - **VF £24/$43**

CRB535A: Barbaric
versions of CRB534
and CRB535
- **VF £16/$30**

CRB536:
VF £26/$47

CRB537: The Double
Centenionalis -
VF £96/$175

CRB537A: The
Centenionalis. As
CRB537 but smaller.
Flan size as obverse B
- **VF £48/$85**

DECENTIUS
Caesar 351 - 353 AD. Brother of Magnentius.

CRB538: as CRB535 - **VF £36/$65**
CRB539: as CRB537 - **VF £120/$215**
CRB539A: as CRB537A - **VF £60/$110**

VETRANIO - 350 AD
Stood against Magnentius in support of Constantius II.

CRB540: - **VF £170/$305**

CONSTANTIUS GALLUS
Caesar 351 - 354 AD. A Cousin of Constantius II.

CRB541: Falling Horseman type,
as CRB532 - **VF £28/$50**

CRB541A: as CRB532A - **VF £20/$35**

Obverse A　　　**Obverse B**

JULIAN II - 360 - 363 AD
Nephew of Constantine I.

Period 1, as Caesar 355 -360 AD

Obverse A

CRB542: Falling Horseman type,
as CRB532A - **VF £18/$32**

CRB543: as CRB531 - **VF £15/$27**

Period 2, as Augustus

CRB544: as CRB531 - **VF £18/$32**

Obverse B　　　**Obverse C**　　　**Obverse D**

CRB545: **VF £80/$145**
(with obverse B)

CRB546: **VF £18/$32**
(with obverse C)

JOVIAN - 363 - 364 AD

CRB547: **VF**
£55/$100

CRB547A:
VF £55/$100

VALENTINIAN I - 364 - 375 AD

Valentinian divided the Empire with his brother Valens. Valentinian ruled the West.

CRB548:	CRB549:	CRB550:	CRB551:
VF £8/$15	VF £8/$15	VF £14/$25	VF £12/$22

VALENS - 364 - 378 AD

Valens ruled the East and minted the same coin types as his brother Valentinian.

CRB552: as CRB548 - **VF £8/$15**
CRB553: as CRB549 - **VF £8/$15**
CRB554: as CRB550 - **VF £14/$25**
CRB555: as CRB551 - **VF £12/$22**

GRATIAN - 367 - 383 AD

Son of Valentinian I. Ruled in the West with his father, until 375.

Obverse A	Obverse B	Obverse C	Obverse D

CRB556: as CRB548 - **VF £11/$20** **CRB557:** as CRB549 - **VF £11/$20**

CRB558:	CRB559: And similar types	CRB560:
VF £13/$23	- VF £9/$15	VF £15/$27

CRB561: Roma Seated	CRB562:	CRB563:	CRB564:
- VF £15/$27	Constantinople Seated	VF £26/$47	VF £22/$40
	- VF £15/$27	(with obverse D)	

VALENTINIAN II - 375 - 392 AD

Son of Valentinian I. Shared rule in the West with Gratian until 383 AD.
His obverse legends are usually the same as those of his father!

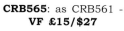

CRB565: as CRB561 -
VF £15/$27

CRB566: as CRB562 -
VF £15/$27

CRB567: as CRB563 -
VF £26/$47 (with obverse C)

Obverse A   Obverse B   Obverse C

CRB568: as CRB564 -
VF £22/$40

CRB569:
VF £16/$30

CRB570:
VF £22/$40

CRB571: And
similar types
- VF £9/$15

CRB572:
VF £9/$15

CRB573: VF
£11/$20

CRB574: VF
£13/$23

THEODOSIUS I - 379 - 395 AD

CRB575: as CRB563 -
VF £26/$47
(with obverse C)

CRB576: as CRB564 - VF £22/$40

CRB577: as CRB570 - VF £22/$40

Obverse A   Obverse B   Obverse C

CRB578: as CRB561 - VF £15/$27

CRB579: as CRB562 - VF £15/$27

CRB580: as CRB572 - VF £9/$15

CRB581: as CRB571 - VF £9/$15

CRB582: as CRB574 - VF £13/$23

CRB583:
VF £22/$40

CRB584:
VF £26/$47

FLACCILLA
Married Theodosius 376, died circa 386 AD.

CRB587: as CRB586 but much smaller -
VF £30/$55

CRB585:
VF £55/$100

CRB586:
VF £60/$110

MAGNUS MAXIMUS - 383 - 388 AD
A rebel in the West.

CRB588:
as CRB564
- **VF £50/$90**

CRB590:
VF £26/$47

CRB591:
VF £26/$47

CRB589:
VF £45/$80

FLAVIUS VICTOR - 387 - 388 AD
Son of Magnus Maximus.

CRB592:
VF £60/$110

EUGENIUS - 392 - 394 AD
A "Puppet" Emperor set up by a general called Arbogast (a barbarian).

CRB593:
VF £110/$200

ARCADIUS - 383 - 408 AD
Son of Theodosius I. Ruled in the East

CRB594: as CRB570 -
VF £22/$40

CRB595: as CRB572 -
VF £9/$15

CRB596: as CRB574 -
VF £13/$23

Obverse A   **Obverse B**   **Obverse C**   **Obverse D**

CRB597: as CRB583 - **VF £22/$40**   **CRB598**: as CRB584 - **VF £22/$40**

ARCADIUS (continued)

CRB599:
VF £22/$40
(with obverse C)

CRB600:
VF £18/$32
(with obverse D)

CRB601:
VF £15/$27

CRB602:
VF £11/$20

CRB603:
VF £18/$32

CRB604: And
similar types
- **VF £9/$15**

CRB605:
VF £20/$35

EUDOXIA
Married Arcadius 395 AD. Died 404 AD.

CRB606:
VF £45/$80

CRB607:
VF £45/$80

HONORIUS - 393 - 423 AD
Son of Theodosius I. Ruled in the West.

Obverse A

Obverse B

Obverse C

CRB608: as CRB572 -
VF £11/$20

CRB609: as CRB583 -
VF £22/$40

CRB610: as CRB584 -
VF £22/$40

CRB611: as CRB600 -
VF £20/$35
(with obverse C)
CRB612: as CRB601 -
VF £15/$27

CRB613: as CRB603 -
VF £18/$32

CRB614: as CRB605 -
VF £20/$35

CRB615:
VF £20/$35

THEODOSIUS II - 402 - 450 AD
Son of Theodosius I. Ruled in the West.

Obverses:

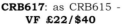
A   **B**

CRB616: as CRB600 -
VF £22/$40
(with obverse B)

CRB617: as CRB615 -
VF £22/$40

CRB618:
VF £20/$35

CRB619:
VF £26/$47

JOHANNES - 423 - 425 AD
Usurper in the West.

CRB620:
VF £125/$225

PHASE FIVE - THE LAST DAYS
The later small bronzes are usually difficult to read and can often be very difficult to attribute correctly.

VALENTINIAN III - 425 - 455 AD
Nephew of Honorius, Emperor in the West.

CRB621:
VF £45/$80

CRB622:
VF £50/$90

MARCIAN - 450 - 457 AD
Emperor in the East.

CRB623: And similar types
- VF £24/$43

LEO - 457 - 474 AD
Emperor in the East.

CRB624:
VF £30/$55

CRB625:
VF £30/$55

CRB626:
VF £30/$55

ZENO - 474 - 491 AD
Emperor in the East.

CRB627:
VF £35/$63

CRB628:
VF £30/$55

BASILISCUS - 475 - 476 AD
Emperor in the East.

ANASTASIUS - 491 - 518 AD
Emperor in the East.

CRB630:
VF £30/$55

CRB629:
VF £65/$115

In 498 AD Anastasius reformed the coinage. This marks the end of the Roman coinage, and the commencement of the Byzantine.

Appendix I. Coin Numbers used in this catalogue

Arranged alphabetically by ruler.

Aelius	142 - 145	Elagabalus	215 - 216
Aemilian	279 - 280	Eudoxia	606 - 607
Agrippa	44	Eugenius	593
Agrippina	50 - 51		
Allectus	346 - 347	Fausta	497 - 498
Anastasius	630	Faustina I	156 - 159
Antonia	46	Faustina II	168 - 171
Antoninus Pius	146 - 155	Flaccilla	585 - 587
Aquilia Severa	218	Flavius Victor	592
Arcadius	594 - 605	Florian	330
Augustus	17 - 31		
Aurelian	320 - 322	Galba	72 - 76
		Galeria Valeria	407
Balbinus	237	Galerius	393 - 406
Basiliscus	629	Gallienus	288 - 294
		Germanicus	47 - 49
Caligula	38 - 40	Geta	203 - 206
Caracalla	197 - 200	Gordian III	239 - 242
Carausius	344 - 345A	Gratian	556 - 564
Carinus	337 - 339		
Carus	334 - 336	Hadrian	128 - 138
Claudius I	53 - 61	Hanniballianus	509
Claudius II	301 - 309	Helena	499 - 500
Clodius Albinus	188 - 189	Herennia Etruscilla	261 - 263
Commodus	175 - 182	Herennius Etruscus	264 - 265
Constans	510 - 519	Honorius	608 - 515
Constantine I	451 - 477	Hostilian	260 - 269
Constantine II	485 - 496		
Constantius I	376 - 392	Johannes	620
Constantius II	520 - 533	Jovian	547
Constantius Gallus	541	Julia Domna	194 - 196
Crispina	183 - 184	Julia Maesa	221 - 222
Crispus	478 - 484	Julia Mamaea	230 - 231
		Julia Paula	217
Decentius	538 - 539	Julia Soaemias	219 - 220
Delmatius	507 - 508	Julia Titi	93
Diadumenian	209 - 210	Julius Caesar	16
Didius Julianus	187		
Diocletian	348 - 359		
Domitian	94 - 110		
Drusus	45		
Drusus (Nero and)	52		

Appendix I. Coin Numbers used in this catalogue

Arranged alphabetically by ruler.

Laelianus	315	Romulus	439 - 440
Leo	624 - 626		
Licinius I	441 - 447A	Sabina	139 - 141
Licinius II	448 - 450	Salonina	295 - 298
Livia	41 - 43	Saloninus	287
Lucilla	175 - 176	Septimius Severus	190 - 193
		Severina	323 - 324
Macrianus	299	Severus II	408 - 416
Macrinus	207 - 208	Severus Alexander	223 - 227
Magnentius	534 - 537		
Magnia Urbica	340	Tacitus	328 - 329
Magnus Maximus	588 - 591	Tetricus I	318
Marcian	623	Tetricus II	319
Marcus Aurelius	160 - 167	Theodora	501
Marius	316	Theodosius I	575 - 584
Maxentius	433 - 438	Theodosius II	616 - 619
Maximianus	360 - 375A	Tiberius	32 - 37
Maximinus I	232 - 234	Titus	87 - 92
Maximinus II	417 - 432	Trajan	117 - 127
Maximus	235 - 236	Trajan Decius	256 - 260
		Trebonianus Gallus	270 - 272
Nero	62 - 71		
Nero and Drusus	52	Vabalathus	327 - 328
Nerva	113 - 116	Valens	552 - 555
Numerian	341 - 343	Valentinian I	548 - 551
		Valentinian II	565 - 574
Octavian (Augustus)	16	Valentinian III	621 - 622
Orbiana	228 - 229	Valerian I	281 - 283
Otacilia Severa	247 - 249	Valerian II	284 - 286
		Verus	172 - 174
Pertinax	185 - 186	Vespasian	79 - 86
Philip I	243 - 246	Vetranio	540
Philip II	250 - 255	Victorinus	317
Plautilla	202	Vitellius	77
Pompey	15	Volusian	273 - 278
Postumus	311 - 314		
Probus	331 - 333	Zeno	627 - 628
Pupienus	238		
Quietus	300		
Quintillus	310		

Appendix II. Mint cities, mid 3rd Century onwards.

On later Roman coins a mint signature will usually be found in the exergue at the bottom of the reverse. Mint-marks begin around the mid 3rd century AD; but come into full use from the time of Diocletian onwards. They consist of an abbreviation of the name of the mint, sometimes preceded by the letters SM (sacred mint), plus usually a variable letter to indicate which workshop at that mint minted any particular coin - as this letter is variable I show it below in italics. Here are some of the mints and mint-marks:

LONDON: *p*LN, *p*LON

TREVERI: (Rhineland) SMTR, *p*TR, TR*p*

AMIENS: AMB

LUGDUNUM: (Lyons) *p*LG LVG*p*

ARELATE/CONSTANTINA: (Arles, S.France). Known between 328 and 340 AD as Constantina. Changed to Arelate in 340 AD, and then back to Constantina in 353 AD. *p*ARL ARL*a* *p*CONST *p*CON

TICINUM: (N.Italy) *p*T

ROME: R*p* SMR*p*

AQUILEIA: (N.Italy) AQ*p* SMAQ*p*

OSTIA: (near Rome) MOST*p*

SISCIA: (Croatia) *a*SIS SISC

SIRMIUM: (Serbia) *a*SIRM

THESSALONIKA: (N.Greece) SMTS*a* TES*a* TS*a*

HERACLEA: (Turkey in Europe, near Constantinople) SMH*a* HERACLA

CONSTANTINOPLE: CONS*a* CONS

NICOMEDIA: (Asiatic Turkey, near Constantinople) SMN*a* MN*a*

CYZICUS: (Asiatic Turkey, near Constantinople) SMK*a*

ANTIOCH: (Turkey, near the Syrian border) SMANT*a* AN*a* ANT*a*

ALEXANDRIA: (Egypt) SMAL*a* ALE*a*

Appendix III. Grading Roman Coins - A rough guide.

The easiest way to determine condition is where there is a portrait.

A well struck coin in Very Fine (VF) condition must show most of the hair, though a small worn patch on the high point is allowable.

In Fine condition one would expect the clear outline of a head with some hair visible.

The legend may be partially off the coin because of the striking, or it may have suffered because of a worn die; but normally one would expect a coin in Very Fine condition to be clearly legible and most of a Fine coin to be more or less readable.

With ancient coins so many other factors can be involved such as toning, a coin being off-centre, having a ragged flan, or a crack, or signs of corrosion. Or a coin may appear worn on one side only because a worn die has been used for that side.

But, other factors apart, a coin in VF condition would normally be worth three times as much as one in Fine condition - or more! In the case of a Nero Sestertius, perhaps six times as much.

Appendix IIII. A suggested cleaning method for
base metal Roman Coins.

The guidance below is offered to people who have purchased uncleaned, or have freshly dug up Roman coins. It is provided as guidance and it should be borne in mind that some coins will always be harder to clean than others. Some will probably be impossible. If patience is not exercised when attempting to clean Roman coins, damage to the coin can result, so for this reason, lots of practice on cheap coins is recommended.

Tools needed:

Stiff nylon brush
Soft brass brush. (test it by rubbing a modern coin first. If it scratches the coin deeply it's probably not soft enough)
Toothpicks
Tap or distilled water
Soap
Olive oil
A water softener product

Important: Base metal Roman coins that have been unearthed have a thin layer of patina on the surface. This naturally occuring patina can be shades of greens or browns, or other colours depending on the soil type the coin was found in. If this layer of patina can be kept intact it will actually make the coin more desirable, as most collectors do not favour coins that have been stripped down to bare metal. For this reason, cleaning the crud off Roman coins, but keeping a layer of what is basically a very thick stain is not always easy.

The cleaning process:

1. Remove any dried dirt with soapy water and a little scrub with the nylon brush. Sometimes soaking the coin in distilled water for a couple of hours will help remove dirt, as the pure distilled water will actually attract the grime. After this step most coins will still be unidentifiable.

2. Ensure the coins are thoroughly dried using a rag, or by leaving them in the air for a length of time. Immerse the coin in olive oil and leave it to soak for at least 4 days (the longer the better). After this soaking, remove the coin and rub it briskly with the soft brass brush, using soap and water. At this stage it may be possible to identify the coin, but if it isn't, leave it to soak again, perhaps for a longer period of time, and then scrub it again with the brass brush and soap and water. Patience is important at this point, as it is better to let the coin soak for longer periods of time, than to scrub it too hard and remove the patina.

3. Often, Roman coins are heavily encrusted with hard stone like mineral deposits. These may require more than a soaking in olive oil to be removed. One quite effective way it to soak the coin for 5-10 minutes in a water softer product, such as Sodium Triphosphate or any number of commercially available products. Ensure the coin doesn't soak for too long as it will risk damaging the coin. Brush the coin with soapy water or gently pick at it with a toothpick and hopefully this will remove the loosened encrustations.

If the coin looks nice enough and can be attributed, then stop. Be prepared to repeat the steps above until a desired result can be achieved, and don't be surprised if some of your coins remain unidentifiable, or if it takes months of patient work and soaking before a coin can be identified.

Where there is verdigris and/or corrosion, try to scrape this off the surface of the coin with a sharp instrument – you might have to dig into the coin, but make sure you get it all out - and then cover with a single drop of clear nail varnish, and rub this in to seal it and prevent reacurrence.

Appendix V. The Imperial Titles and Abbreviations.

The Earlier Empire:

In the earliest days of the Empire the Emperor included both Caesar and Augustus in his own personal titles, but it soon became the custom to give the title "Caesar" to a "second-in-command", and to use "Augustus" as the title of the top man, or of equal ranking top men.

There could be several Caesars and Augusti at the same time, and it will help to note how this can be shown on coins. For example, "the Victory of the Emperor" can be written as VICTORIA AVG; but where there is more than one reigning Emperor this can be shown by adding extra G's - Victoria AVGG means "the Victory of the two Emperors", and VICTORIA AVGGG "the Victory of the three Emperors".

IMP is short for "Imperator", a title given to the commander-in-chief of an army, who, in the time of the Empire, was the Emperor himself (in fact our word "Emperor" is derived from this Latin title). IMP, however, also has another meaning, that of the shout of acclamation given by soldiers to their commander after winning a victory. They would greet him with a shout of "Imperator". As Commander-in-chief, an Emperor would count these "shouts" as being for himself, even when he had been nowhere near the action. Thus we find coins naming Domitian as IMP XXII, meaning that his armies had won twenty-two battles, and Claudius reaching IMP XXVII for 27 victories. Unfortunately these IMP's do not increase at regular intervals, and are of limited use for dating purposes.

COS is an abbreviated form of "Consul". From the beginning of the Roman Republican period way back in 510BC Rome had been ruled by two annually appointed consuls. The earlier Emperors liked to pretend that Rome was still a republic, and continued to have two consuls each year. Frequently the Emperor himself was one of these, and would mark the honour permanently on the coinage by placing COS either after his name on the obverse, or on the reverse. When appointed on a second occasion, he became COS II, and so on – Commodus reached COS VII. If an Emperor was chosen for the consulate, but had not yet entered office he might occasionally mark this on the coinage as COS DES "designated consul". Thus we find Marcus Aurelius as COS DES II in 144AD, meaning that he had served one term as Consul and was soon to become Consul for the second time. As with IMPs COS numbers are of limited use when dating a coin.

Appendix V. The Imperial Titles and Abbreviations.

Our best guide for dating is TRP, or TRIB POT, (short for "Tribunicia Potestas"), which was a title the Emperor did receive annually. Unfortunately we have to know where to start. For example Marcus Aurelius became Caesar in 139AD and Augustus in 161; yet his first Trib Pot was awarded him in 147AD, after which the TRPs rise annually up to his death in 180AD, by which time he had reached TRP XXXIV.

An Emperor was also PM (Pontifex Maximus – "High Priest"), and PP (Pater Patriae – "the father of his country"). An individual Emperor might be awarded a special title, such as PARTHICUS for beating the Parthians in battle, or GERMANICUS or DACICUS; but these are all just of general interest rather than helps to pin down a coin to an exact date.

The abbreviations of the Later Empire:

DN, for "Dominus noster" - Our Lord (the Emperor)

PF, "Pius, Felix" - Faithful and blessed

IVN, - "Junior"

MAX, "Maximus" - Very great

NOB CAES, NOB C, NC - Noble Caesar

A note on Forgeries

Local, often badly made, contemporary copies are probably NOT forgeries. They count as "copies", and were most likely used as currency by someone somewhere at sometime. Remember that forgeries are far more likely to involve the rarer pieces, such as a Nero sestertius showing the "Harbour at Ostia", or a coin of Pertinax, who reigned for a few days in 193AD, than an antoninianus of someone like Tetricus I. When offered a rarer coin, unless the dealer is a reputable one, always have a suspicious mind.

Those we must beware of are modern productions, usually, though not always (as in the case of the mid-16th century "Paduan copies" which were meant as examples of ancient art), meant to deceive the collector.

Watch out for the cast copy. Look for "pitting" on the coin surface caused by air bubbles occuring during the casting process; and examine for signs of a possible telltale line round the edge, where two halves have been cast separately and then joined together.

Weight can usually be a good guide with gold or silver where difference between one coin and another of the same denomination is normally small; but this does NOT apply to base metal, though if a coin is much lighter or heavier than others of the same type, this may be suspicious.

Even more suspicious is when the coin you are offered is "unique". If your coin is base metal and all the other known examples are gold; or if it consists of two reverse types, have you really got something unique?

If the coin is too perfect, perhaps too round – be careful!

All collectors, I am sure, have been caught out by a fake at one time or another. Some forgeries are so good that even the big dealers have been deceived! Look at, and if possible, handle a lot of coins so as to "get the feel" of the genuine article, and hopefully you will not be "caught out" too often.

The Cover Coin

The coin shown on the front and back covers of this book is a Constantine the Great, Campgate type, Bronze AE 3 in choice Extremely Fine condition. It weighs 3.224g is 18.9mm in diameter and was made at the Siscia mint between 326 - 327 AD. In this book the coin is CRB469 (with obverse D). This choice EF example was sold by www.forumancientcoins.com for US$150 (about £85).